Get set for the new KS2 SATS with CGP!

This CGP book is packed with short, sharp tests for KS2 grammar, punctuation and spelling. They're brilliant practice for the new Year 6 English SATS in 2016 and beyond!

For more practice at the same level of difficulty, Book 1 is also available.

The tests are just like mini versions of the real SATS — we've even included pull-out scripts for each spelling test. If you'd rather not read these out yourself, you can download full audio files from:

www.cgpbooks.co.uk/ks210mintests

What CGP is all about

Our sole aim here at CGP is to produce the highest quality books — carefully written, immaculately presented and dangerously close to being funny.

Then we work our socks off to get them out to you — at the cheapest possible prices.

Contents

Set C

The transcripts for the spelling tests can be
found in a pull-out section in the middle of the
book, or you can use the online audio files.

Published by CGP

Editors: Kirstie McHale, Sarah Oxley, Caley Simpson
With thanks to Lucy Loveluck and Janet Berkeley for the proofreading.

ISBN: 978 1 78294 478 2
Clipart from Corel®
Printed by Elanders Ltd, Newcastle upon Tyne.
Based on the classic CGP style created by Richard Parsons.

Set A: Grammar & Punctuation 1

There are **12 questions** in this test. Give yourself **10 minutes** to answer them all.

1.   Circle the **verb** in the sentence below.

I listened to some music.

_____

1 mark

2.   Tick the sentence below that uses **capital letters** correctly.

tick **one** box

On Mondays, steven plays football in the Park.   ☐

On mondays, Steven plays Football in the park.   ☐

on Mondays, Steven plays football in the Park.   ☐

On Mondays, Steven plays football in the park.   ☐

_____

1 mark

3.   Draw a line to match each word to its correct **antonym**.

Word	Antonym
genuine	abundant
meagre	insincere
inferior	exceptional

_____

1 mark

4. Read the sentence below. Circle the **modal verb** in the brackets which completes the sentence so that it indicates **certainty**.

The dog (might / should / will) need a bath
after going for a walk in the forest.

_____
1 mark

5. Complete the sentence below using a **possessive pronoun**.

Those shoes aren't ....·

_____
1 mark

6. Add a **colon** to the sentence below so that it is punctuated correctly.

The netball team was going to be late their bus
had broken down.

_____
1 mark

7. Underline the **noun phrase** in the sentence below.

One of the children wasn't listening.

_____
1 mark

8.   Circle the **preposition** in each sentence below.

Geri often hid behind the door.

Ben has played the guitar since September.

9.   Tick the sentence below that uses **direct speech** correctly.

	tick **one** box
I asked "can we go shopping on Saturday"?	☐
I asked, "Can we go shopping on Saturday"?	☐
I asked "can we go shopping on Saturday?"	☐
I asked, "Can we go shopping on Saturday?"	☐

10.   Rewrite the sentence below in the **active voice**.

The tadpoles were bullied by the frogs.

....

....

11. Read the sentence below. Tick the box that uses **apostrophes** correctly to complete the sentence.

They counted .... in the sports hall.

tick **one** box

peoples vote's	☐
people's votes	☐
peoples' votes	☐
peoples' vote's	☐

12. Complete the table below by writing suitable words in the empty boxes. The first one has been done for you.

Verb	Adjective
succeed	successful
believe	
invent	

END OF TEST

/ 12

There are **12 questions** in this test. Give yourself **10 minutes** to answer them all.

1. Read the sentence below. Write the **contracted form** of the underlined words in the box.

    I <u>will not</u> go to the shops.

    [   ]

    _____
    1 mark

2. Tick the sentence below that should end with a **question mark**.

    tick **one** box

    I don't know who to ask   [ ]

    They aren't sure how it happened   [ ]

    Where's the train station   [ ]

    What I saw was simply amazing   [ ]

    _____
    1 mark

3. Underline the **object** in the sentence below.

    Coralie found Nigel.

    _____
    1 mark

4. Add a **semi-colon** to the sentence below so that it's punctuated correctly.

The library at the end of my street is closed on Wednesday afternoons the library in town is closed on Monday afternoons.

1 mark

5. Read the sentences below. Tick the **two** sentences where the word <u>delay</u> is used as a **noun**.

tick **two** boxes

The pilot had to delay the plane's take-off. ☐

The company apologised for the delay. ☐

There was a delay in getting the results. ☐

Joe did not allow the bad weather to delay his trip. ☐

1 mark

6. Tick the sentence below that uses the **present progressive** tense.

tick **one** box

I play football every Thursday. ☐

I was watching television. ☐

She wished she could go on holiday. ☐

They are making lunch for us. ☐

1 mark

7. Underline the **subordinate clause** in the sentence below.

I didn't want to take part in the school play because I'm too shy.

1 mark

8. Tick the pair of **verbs** that best completes the sentence below.

Sparrows .... once commonly found in gardens, but now they .... a rarer sight in this country.

tick **one** box

were	were	☐
were	is	☐
were	are	☐
was	are	☐

1 mark

9. Explain how the **commas** used below give the two sentences different meanings.

All the children who are blond enjoy swimming.

All the children, who are blond, enjoy swimming.

....

....

....

1 mark

10. Read the sentence below.
Circle the **present perfect** form of the underlined verb.

He <u>writes</u> in his diary every night.

wrote   will write   had written   has written

_____
1 mark

11. Draw a line to match each word to the correct **synonym**.

Word	Synonym
disappointed	content
impolite	livid
happy	disrespectful
furious	disheartened

_____
1 mark

12. Write a sentence below that has two **determiners**.
Underline the determiners in your sentence.

....

....

_____
1 mark

END OF TEST

/ 12

There are **12 questions** in this test. Give yourself **10 minutes** to answer them all.

1. Read the sentence below. Tick **one** box to label the **adjective** in the sentence.

    There was a red box lying on the floor.

    _____
    1 mark

2. Underline the **main clause** in the sentence below.

    Francis enjoys going for walks in the countryside, even though he has a bad knee.

    _____
    1 mark

3. Rewrite the two sentences below as **one** sentence by adding a **conjunction**.

    We could go shopping. We could go bowling.

    ....

    ....

    _____
    1 mark

4. The sentence below is missing a **comma**.
    Tick **one** box to show where the comma should go.

    □   □

    I made a fruit salad using melons grapes and strawberries.

    □   □

    _____
    1 mark

5. Tick the sentence below that uses **tenses** correctly.

                                                        tick **one** box

    I am playing tennis and then I went out for a meal.   □

    I played tennis and then I went out for a meal.   □

    I play tennis and then I went out for a meal.   □

    I will play tennis and then I went out for a meal.   □

    _____
    1 mark

6. Circle the **relative pronoun** in the sentence below.

    I was asked to speak in assembly by my teacher,
    who is in charge of assemblies.

    _____
    1 mark

7. Add a **comma** to the sentence below so that it's punctuated correctly.

Before he could stop me I snatched a cake and ate it.

1 mark

8. Put a tick in the correct column to show whether each sentence is a **command** or a **statement**. One has already been done for you.

Sentence	Command	Statement
You could take the rubbish out.		✓
Water the plants.		
My brother washes the car.		
Lily, put those books away.		

1 mark

9. Explain how the **hyphen** used below gives the two sentences different meanings.

Sally had to hand in four weekly reports.

Sally had to hand in four-weekly reports.

....

....

....

1 mark

10. Complete the sentence below using an **adverb**.

" .... we could paint your room blue," said Mum.

_____
1 mark

11. Draw a line to match each **prefix** to a word to make a new word.
The first one has been done for you.

| auto | ———————— | biography |

| super | | lead |

| anti | | act |

| mis | | clockwise |

| inter | | visor |

_____
1 mark

12. Tick the **two** sentences below that use the **subjunctive** form.

tick **two** boxes

If I were you, I would enter the competition. ☐

Shall I bring my tent? ☐

If it's too heavy, I'll take it for you. ☐

I wish I were able to go with you. ☐

_____
1 mark

END OF TEST

/ 12

There are **12 questions** in this test. Give yourself **10 minutes** to answer them all.

1. Circle the **verb** from the list below which completes the sentence using **Standard English**.

    They .... watching the film in silence.

    were   was   is   will

    _____
    1 mark

2. Tick **three** boxes to show the **nouns** in the sentence below.

    It was warm, so the team were playing all of their

    matches on the field.

    _____
    1 mark

3. Complete the sentence below using the correct **punctuation mark**.

    What an enormous cow that is

    _____
    1 mark

4. Circle the **conjunction** in the sentence below.

Since it was raining outside, I decided to stay in
and draw a picture.

5. Draw a line to match each sentence with the **tense** it is written in.

Sentence	Tense
I was watching TV with my sister.	simple past
The cat hid under the sofa.	simple present
She isn't here at the moment.	past progressive

6. Rewrite the sentence below as a **command**.

Can you tidy your bedroom after you've washed the dishes?

....

....

7. Circle all the **pronouns** in the sentence below.

She felt very sorry for herself after falling into our pool.

8. Read the sentence below and underline the **relative clause**.

My auntie, who lives in France, likes to visit the market.

9. Tick the sentence below that uses a **dash** correctly.

tick **one** box

Hartford is the state capital of Connecticut it's about halfway — between New York and Boston.	☐
Hartford is the state capital of Connecticut — it's about halfway between New York and Boston.	☐
Hartford is the state capital of Connecticut it's about halfway between — New York and Boston.	☐
Hartford — is the state capital of Connecticut it's about halfway between New York and Boston.	☐

1 mark

10. Put a letter in each box to show which **word class** the words belong to.

| adjective X | adverb Y | verb Z |

Taylor gently stroked her cat — they were both relaxed.

1 mark

11. Add a pair of **brackets** to the sentence below so that it is punctuated correctly.

We went to the beach I forgot my sun hat, as usual and spent the afternoon swimming and sunbathing.

1 mark

12. Draw a line to match each word to the correct **suffix** to make a new word.

pray   able

respect   ment

different   er

equip   ly

1 mark

END OF TEST

/ 12

Set A: Grammar & Punctuation 4

Set A: Spelling Test

For this test, you'll need someone to **read out** the transcript from the middle of the book, or you can use the **online audio file**. The test will take about 10 minutes.

mark box

1. There were seven .... on the committee. ☐

2. Luke had to .... the flour very carefully. ☐

3. The .... in England is the pound. ☐

4. The dress fitted .... ☐

5. Mala was not .... to go to the party. ☐

6. Anna didn't want to .... any words. ☐

7. Philip saw a .... when he went to Egypt. ☐

8. The school council had a .... ☐

9. Sadie's laughter was .... ☐

10. It's an .... hexagon. ☐

11. The shop assistant gave Tamal a .... ☐

12. Rob was flattered by the .... ☐

/ 12

End of Set A: Scoresheet

You've finished a full set of tests — well done!

Now it's time to put your scores in here
and see how you're getting on.

	Score	
Test 1		/12
Test 2		/12
Test 3		/12
Test 4		/12
Spelling Test		/12
Total		**/60**

Once you've got a score out of 60, check it out in the table below...

0 – 29	If you got a lot of questions wrong, don't worry. Ask an adult to help you work out the **areas** you need **more practice** on. Then have another go at **this** set of tests.
30 – 45	If you got half-marks or better, you're doing well. **Read** back over your **incorrect** answers and make sure you know **why** they're wrong. Then try the **next set** of tests.
46 – 60	Woohoo! Now have a go at the **next set** of tests — can you beat your score?

But before you do... bend your brain round this one:

Fill in the sentence below using the words 'where', 'wear' and 'were'.

We .... going to a museum .... we could .... clothes
from the Tudor period.

There are **12 questions** in this test. Give yourself **10 minutes** to answer them all.

1.   Read the sentences below. Circle **one** word in each pair of brackets to complete the sentences using **Standard English**.

He should (have / of) been here by now.

I don't know (nothing / anything) about that.

_____
1 mark

2.   Tick **both** sentences below that use the word <u>notice</u> as a **verb**.

tick **two** boxes

Did you notice the sign on the door? ☐

She put a notice up on the board at school. ☐

I handed in my notice at work. ☐

It took them a week to notice. ☐

_____
1 mark

3.   Complete the sentence below by adding suitable **determiners**.

I asked for .... ice cream with .... chocolate flake, but .... shop was closed.

_____
1 mark

4.   Underline the **main clause** in each of the sentences below.

While Nate is shopping, Liza takes the dog for a walk.

I didn't buy a handbag, although I did see one that I liked.

_____
1 mark

5. Rewrite the sentence below as a **question**.

Turn off the television!

....

....

1 mark

6. Put a tick in each row to show whether each sentence is in the **active** or **passive** voice. One has already been done for you.

Sentence	Active	Passive
They were surprised by the response.		✔
I was welcomed by the head teacher.		
The man juggled with the apples.		
I dragged my suitcase down the street.		

1 mark

7. Rewrite the sentence below using the correct punctuation for **direct speech**.

i shouted watch out for that dog

....

....

1 mark

8. Tick the sentence below that uses the **past progressive** tense.

                                                    tick **one** box

    I will be going to France next week.   ☐

    David is making dinner.   ☐

    Nadiya was walking home.   ☐

    Paul reads a book.   ☐

                                                    _____
                                                    1 mark

9. Circle the **subordinating conjunction** and underline
    the **co-ordinating conjunction** in the sentence below.

    The swimming pool is busy when it's the
    summer holidays, and you have to queue to get in.   _____
                                                            1 mark

10. Read the two sentences below. Explain how the use of a
    comma changes the meaning of the second sentence.

    Are you going to tell Gareth?
    Are you going to tell, Gareth?

    ....

    ....

    ....
                                                            _____
                                                            1 mark

11. Circle the two words that are **antonyms** of each other in the passage below.

As I walked onto the big stage, I felt really anxious. I looked out at the expectant faces in the crowd. Mum caught my eye with her confident gaze, and I felt better.

12. Put a tick in each row to show whether the underlined word in each sentence is a **conjunction** or a **preposition**.

Sentence	Conjunction	Preposition
I'll take an umbrella <u>as</u> it's raining.		
She bought it <u>as</u> a present.		
He waved <u>as</u> he left the room.		

1 mark

END OF TEST

/ 12

There are **12 questions** in this test. Give yourself **10 minutes** to answer them all.

1. Tick the sentence below that should end with a **question mark**.

                                                        tick **one** box

    I couldn't hear the music   ☐

    What surprised me was how busy it was   ☐

    Hal didn't know what to do   ☐

    Becky likes carrot cake, doesn't she   ☐

    _____
    1 mark

2. Rewrite the passage below with the correct
    capital letters and **full stops**.

    the wind howled as james wrapped his scarf tighter he was
    looking forward to getting home and warming up

    ....

    ....

    ....

    ....

    _____
    1 mark

3. Circle all the **verbs** in the passage below.

    Amar runs twice every week. He ran 3 kilometres

    yesterday — he was tired afterwards.   _____
    1 mark

4.   The sentence below is missing a **dash**.
     Tick **one** box to show where the dash should go.

     Luis bought himself a bike he had just been paid.

     ⬆   ⬆   ⬆

     ☐   ☐   ☐

                                                                    _____
                                                                    1 mark

5.   Read the sentence below.
     Underline the longest **noun phrase** there is in the sentence.

     I couldn't reach the book on the top shelf.   _____
                                                                    1 mark

6.   Circle the **conjunction** in each sentence below.

     Jon's bat was broken so he could not play cricket.

     Whilst watching TV, he dropped crumbs on the carpet.

     Since he was late, he decided not to buy a paper.   _____
                                                                    1 mark

7.   Underline the **subject** of the sentence below.

     The librarian couldn't find the book on the civil war.   _____
                                                                    1 mark

8.   Add a **comma** to the sentence below so that it's punctuated correctly.

As quietly as possible I crept out of the room.

1 mark

9.   Read the passage below. Underline the verb form that's in the
present perfect tense.

I was disappointed when I wasn't chosen for the school
cheerleading team. I have auditioned for the school choir,
so I'm hoping that I'll be selected for that instead.

1 mark

10. Read the sentence below.
Tick the word that is the closest **synonym** of the word 'vulnerable'.

There are many <u>vulnerable</u> species, which need to be protected.

tick **one** box

safe   ☐

volatile   ☐

endangered   ☐

dangerous   ☐

1 mark

11. Complete the sentence below so that it uses the **subjunctive** form.

If I .... taller, I would be allowed to
go on the rollercoaster.

_____
1 mark

12. Look at the **word family** below. What does the root <u>vac</u> mean?

vacant   evacuate   vacancy

tick **one** box

empty   ☐

busy   ☐

move   ☐

motion   ☐

_____
1 mark

END OF TEST

/ 12

There are **12 questions** in this test. Give yourself **10 minutes** to answer them all.

1. Read the sentence below, then insert **commas** so that it's punctuated correctly.

   I went to the shops and bought a pen some trousers a T-shirt a pair of shoes and a DVD.

   _____
   1 mark

2. Circle the **adverb** in the sentence below.

   Afterwards, we went out for a meal and I ate a large pizza.

   _____
   1 mark

3. Tick the pair of **verbs** that best completes the sentence below.

   My teacher .... me to write a poem, so I .... one about the countryside.

   tick **one** box

   asking   writing   ☐

   asked   write   ☐

   asks   wrote   ☐

   asked   wrote   ☐

   _____
   1 mark

4. Circle the **co-ordinating conjunction** in each sentence below.

My brother is 8 years old, and I am 10 years old.

I want a pet, but my parents won't let me have one.

We could have chips for tea, or we could have pasta. _____

1 mark

5. Which punctuation mark should be used in the place indicated by the arrow in the sentence below?

There are several things I'd like to do this weekend go shopping,

go to the cinema, have a sleepover and play netball.

tick **one** box

full stop ☐

comma ☐

colon ☐

semi-colon ☐

1 mark

6. Write a sentence below using the word <u>walk</u> as a **noun**.

....

....

1 mark

7. Which of the sentences below is punctuated correctly?

tick **one** box

Angel Falls which is in Venezuela — is the highest waterfall — in the world. ☐

Angel Falls — which is in Venezuela — is the highest waterfall in the world. ☐

Angel Falls which is in Venezuela — is the highest waterfall in the world. ☐

Angel Falls — which is in Venezuela is the highest waterfall — in the world. ☐

_____
1 mark

8. Write down the **suffix** which can be added to **all** of the nouns below to make verbs.

| advert | real | final | idol |

....

_____
1 mark

9. Put a tick in the correct column to show whether the underlined word is an **adjective** or an **adverb**.

Sentence	Adjective	Adverb
Elliot is a <u>good</u> singer.		
She acted <u>well</u> in the play.		
That exercise is really <u>easy</u>.		

_____
1 mark

10. Circle the **relative pronoun** in the sentence below.

My friends are going to a festival, which is in the field beside the church.

_____
1 mark

11. Underline the **subordinate clause** in the sentence below.

I stayed up watching television until it was late.

_____
1 mark

12. Rewrite the sentence below in the **passive voice**.

Over a million people watched the final on television.

....

....

_____
1 mark

END OF TEST

/ 12

There are **11 questions** in this test. Give yourself **10 minutes** to answer them all.

1. Complete the table by writing the **contracted form** of each pair of words. The first one has been done for you.

Words	Contracted form
we have	we've
he has	
will not	

1 mark

2. Draw a line to match each sentence with the most likely final **punctuation mark**. You can only use each punctuation mark **once**.

What a mess	.
What are you saying	?
What I meant was that we should leave soon	!

1 mark

3. Circle all the **pronouns** in the passage below.

Nia and Fred were at the zoo. They saw lots of animals.
Nia liked the tigers, so she bought a tiger key ring.

1 mark

Key Stage 2
10-Minute Tests
Spelling Test Transcripts

The spelling tests need to be **read out loud** to the children.

You can read the tests out loud to the children by following the instructions below, or you can play an **audio file** from here:

www.cgpbooks.co.uk/ks210mintests

Each test should take about 10 minutes.

For each test, read out the following instructions, and then answer any questions the children have.

- *Listen to the instructions I'm about to give you.*
- *I'm going to read out twelve sentences. These sentences are printed on your answer page, but each one has a word missing. Listen to the missing word and write it in. Make sure you spell it correctly.*
- *I will read the word, then read the word within a sentence, then I'll say the word a third time.*
- *The test will now begin.*

Now read the spellings to the children:

- *Say the spelling number.*
- *Say "The word is..."*
- *Read out the word in its sentence.*
- *Say "The word is..."*
- *Pause for at least 12 seconds between each of the spellings.*

At the end of each test, read out all 12 sentences again, and give the children time to change their answers if they want to.

When the test is over, say "This is the end of the test."

Set A: Spelling Questions

Read out the instructions from the **first page** of this pull-out. Then read out the following:

1. Spelling one.
   The word is **ladies**.
   *There were seven **ladies** on the committee.*
   The word is **ladies**.

2. Spelling two.
   The word is **weigh**.
   *Luke had to **weigh** the flour*
   very carefully.
   The word is **weigh**.

3. Spelling three.
   The word is **currency**.
   *The **currency** in England is the pound.*
   The word is **currency**.

4. Spelling four.
   The word is **perfectly**.
   *The dress fitted **perfectly**.*
   The word is **perfectly**.

5. Spelling five.
   The word is **allowed**.
   *Mala was not **allowed** to go to the party.*
   The word is **allowed**.

6. Spelling six.
   The word is **misspell**.
   *Anna didn't want to **misspell** any words.*
   The word is **misspell**.

7. Spelling seven.
   The word is **pyramid**.
   *Philip saw a **pyramid** when he went to Egypt.*
   The word is **pyramid**.

8. Spelling eight.
   The word is **discussion**.
   *The school council had a **discussion**.*
   The word is **discussion**.

9. Spelling nine.
   The word is **infectious**.
   *Sadie's laughter was **infectious**.*
   The word is **infectious**.

10. Spelling ten.
    The word is **irregular**.
    *It's an **irregular** hexagon.*
    The word is **irregular**.

11. Spelling eleven.
    The word is **receipt**.
    *The shop assistant gave Tamal a **receipt**.*
    The word is **receipt**.

12. Spelling twelve.
    The word is **compliment**.
    *Rob was flattered by the **compliment**.*
    The word is **compliment**.

At the end of the test, read out **all 12** sentences again, and give the children time to change their answers if they want to.
When the test is over, say "This is the end of the test."

Set B: Spelling Questions

Read out the instructions from the **first page** of this pull-out. Then read out the following:

1. Spelling one.
   The word is **quiet**.
   *It was very **quiet** in the library.*
   The word is **quiet**.

2. Spelling two.
   The word is **nature**.
   *Class One were going to a **nature** reserve.*
   The word is **nature**.

3. Spelling three.
   The word is **division**.
   *Ally uses a calculator for **division** questions.*
   The word is **division**.

4. Spelling four.
   The word is **couple**.
   *Vicky went to the dance class a **couple** of times.*
   The word is **couple**.

5. Spelling five.
   The word is **sensation**.
   *Flying in a plane was a new **sensation** for Talia.*
   The word is **sensation**.

6. Spelling six.
   The word is **character**.
   *Alan's behaviour was out of **character**.*
   The word is **character**.

7. Spelling seven.
   The word is **preferably**.
   *Padma wanted a sandwich, **preferably** a cheese one.*
   The word is **preferably**.

8. Spelling eight.
   The word is **creation**.
   *The baker admired his **creation**.*
   The word is **creation**.

9. Spelling nine.
   The word is **curious**.
   *George was a **curious** child.*
   The word is **curious**.

10. Spelling ten.
    The word is **partial**.
    *Sarah was **partial** to a slice of cake.*
    The word is **partial**.

11. Spelling eleven.
    The word is **responsibly**.
    *Becky always behaved **responsibly**.*
    The word is **responsibly**.

12. Spelling twelve.
    The word is **muscles**.
    *Neil's **muscles** were sore after a ten-mile run.*
    The word is **muscles**.

At the end of the test, read out **all 12** sentences again, and give the children time to change their answers if they want to.

When the test is over, say "This is the end of the test."

Set C: Spelling Questions

Read out the instructions from the **first page** of this pull-out. Then read out the following:

1. Spelling one.
   The word is **hopping**.
   *A frog was **hopping** across the garden.*
   The word is **hopping**.

2. Spelling two.
   The word is **crawl**.
   *Jenny's baby brother is learning to **crawl**.*
   The word is **crawl**.

3. Spelling three.
   The word is **headquarters**.
   *The scout **headquarters** were
   a bit shabby.*
   The word is **headquarters**.

4. Spelling four.
   The word is **science**.
   *Shamir was doing a **science** experiment.*
   The word is **science**.

5. Spelling five.
   The word is **hungrily**.
   *David looked **hungrily** at
   the chocolate cake.*
   The word is **hungrily**.

6. Spelling six.
   The word is **electrician**.
   *The **electrician** came to fit
   some new plug sockets.*
   The word is **electrician**.

7. Spelling seven.
   The word is **antique**.
   *Anita's kitchen table is an **antique**.*
   The word is **antique**.

8. Spelling eight.
   The word is **brochures**.
   *The travel agent gave them
   some holiday **brochures**.*
   The word is **brochures**.

9. Spelling nine.
   The word is **protein**.
   *It's important to have enough
   protein in your diet.*
   The word is **protein**.

10. Spelling ten.
    The word is **plough**.
    *The farmer went to **plough** the field.*
    The word is **plough**.

11. Spelling eleven.
    The word is **glamorous**.
    *Everyone at the ball looked very **glamorous**.*
    The word is **glamorous**.

12. Spelling twelve.
    The word is **exaggerate**.
    *The fisherman was told not to **exaggerate**.*
    The word is **exaggerate**.

At the end of the test, read out **all 12** sentences again, and give the children time to change their answers if they want to.
When the test is over, say "This is the end of the test."

4. Tick the ending below that turns the word <u>care</u> into an **adjective**.

tick **one** box

care**ful** ☐

car**ingly** ☐

care**fully** ☐

care**r** ☐

_____
1 mark

5. Circle the **modal verb** in the sentence below.

They could be here at six o'clock.

_____
1 mark

Does the modal verb you circled indicate **certainty** or **possibility**?

☐

_____
1 mark

6. Which word does **not** make a new word when you add the prefix '**un**'?

tick **one** box

happy ☐

belief ☐

inspired ☐

kind ☐

_____
1 mark

7.   Tick the **option** below that completes this sentence in the
     simple past tense.

     The puppies .... about on the floor.

                         tick **one** box

     were rolling   ☐

     was rolling   ☐

     rolled   ☐

     have rolled   ☐
                                                              _____
                                                              1 mark

8.   Underline the **adverbial** in the sentence below.

     My grandad walks with a limp — he has an old injury.   _____
                                                              1 mark

9.   Rewrite the list below in **bullet point** form.
     Remember to punctuate your answer correctly.

     I need to wash the dishes, tidy my room
     and take the dog for a walk.

     Things I need to do:

     •   ....

     •   ....

     •   ....   _____
                                                                                1 mark

10. Rewrite the sentence below in the **passive** voice.

Tom ate the tomatoes.

....

....
_____
1 mark

11. Tick the sentence below that uses **semi-colons** correctly.

tick **one** box

I ate fish, chips and peas on Monday; a chicken wrap on Tuesday; and potatoes, sausages and beans on Wednesday. ☐

I ate fish; chips and peas on Monday; a chicken wrap on Tuesday; and potatoes; sausages and beans on Wednesday. ☐

I ate; fish chips and peas on Monday, a chicken wrap on Tuesday, and potatoes; sausages and beans on Wednesday. ☐
_____
1 mark

END OF TEST

/ 12

Set B: Grammar & Punctuation 4

For this test, you'll need someone to **read out** the transcript from the middle of the book, or you can use the **online audio file**. The test will take about 10 minutes.

mark box

1. It was very .... in the library. ☐

2. Class One were going to a .... reserve. ☐

3. Ally uses a calculator for .... questions. ☐

4. Vicky went to the dance class a .... of times. ☐

5. Flying in a plane was a new .... for Talia. ☐

6. Alan's behaviour was out of .... ☐

7. Padma wanted a sandwich, ... a cheese one. ☐

8. The baker admired his .... ☐

9. George was a .... child. ☐

10. Sarah was .... to a slice of cake. ☐

11. Becky always behaved .... ☐

12. Neil's .... were sore after a ten-mile run. ☐

/ 12

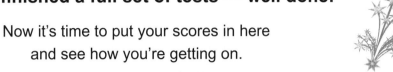

End of Set B: Scoresheet

You've finished a full set of tests — well done!

Now it's time to put your scores in here
and see how you're getting on.

	Score	
Test 1		/12
Test 2		/12
Test 3		/12
Test 4		/12
Spelling Test		/12
Total		**/60**

Once you've got a score out of 60, check it out in the table below...

0 – 29	If you got a lot of questions wrong, don't worry. Ask an adult to help you work out the **areas** you need **more practice** on. Then have another go at **this** set of tests.
30 – 45	If you got half-marks or better, you're doing well. **Read** back over your **incorrect** answers and make sure you know **why** they're wrong. Then try the **next set** of tests.
46 – 60	Woohoo! Now have a go at the **next set** of tests — can you beat your score?

But before you do... bend your brain round this one:

Turn 'A' into 'ASHAMED' by adding letters one at a time to the start
or the end of the word. At each step, you must make a new word.

A   <u>A</u> <u>M</u>   _ _ _   _ _ _ _   _ _ _ _ _   _ _ _ _ _ _   ASHAMED

Set C: Grammar & Punctuation 1

There are **12 questions** in this test. Give yourself **10 minutes** to answer them all.

1. Tick the sentence below which is most likely to end with an **exclamation mark**.

    tick **one** box

    Can I have an apple please ☐

    Put that down right now ☐

    What do you want for tea ☐

    The weather was fine ☐

    _____
    1 mark

2. The sentence below is missing **speech marks**.
   Add speech marks so that the sentence is punctuated correctly.

    That's a really nice backpack, said Nita.

    _____
    1 mark

3. Tick the sentence below that is a **command**.

    tick **one** box

    I asked you to empty the dishwasher. ☐

    Would you like to make Hilary a cup of tea? ☐

    I don't believe it! ☐

    Put the lid on before you shake it. ☐

    _____
    1 mark

4. Circle the **adjective** in the sentence below.

Before she tidied it, Lucy's room was messier
than Sam's room.

_____

1 mark

5. Tick the sentence below that uses an **apostrophe** correctly.

tick **one** box

I borrowed Robs armband's for swimming. ☐

I borrowed Robs' armbands for swimming. ☐

I borrowed Rob's armbands for swimming. ☐

I borrowed Robs armbands' for swimming. ☐

_____

1 mark

6. Rewrite the statement below as a **question**.

Bluebells are usually found in wooded areas.

....

....

_____

1 mark

39

7.   Underline the **conjunction** in the sentence below.

Last night I read my book until I fell asleep.

1 mark

8.   Complete the sentence below with a suitable **possessive pronoun**.

Jo thought the jumper was .... , but she wasn't sure.

1 mark

9.   Draw a line to join each **prefix** to a verb in order to make a new verb.

Prefix	Verb
dis	clip
un	clutter
mis	agree
de	judge

1 mark

10.   Underline the **main clause** in each of the sentences below.

Arthur made Kirstie pancakes on her birthday.

Before Kamil went to Rome, he bought an Italian dictionary.

1 mark

11. Tick the sentence below that uses the word <u>light</u> as a **noun**.

tick **one** box

The duvet felt as light as a feather. ☐

Sam said he would light the bonfire early. ☐

Turn off the light before he sees us! ☐

Jasmine painted her bedroom walls light pink. ☐

_____

1 mark

12. Circle the **three** words below that are in the same **word family**.

Henry and Lauren had floral arrangements on the
tables at their wedding. They had trouble finding
a florist at first, but they managed to sort it out
in the end. The flowers were beautiful.

_____

1 mark

END OF TEST

/ 12

There are **11 questions** in this test. Give yourself **10 minutes** to answer them all.

1. Read the passage below. Insert **capital letters** and **full stops** so that the passage is punctuated correctly.
One has already been done for you.

T
ᴛony and will spent ages pulling up weeds in the garden last saturday it looked much better when they were finished

_____
1 mark

2. Read the sentence below.
Tick the pair of **verbs** which best complete the sentence.

Last week, I .... to the cinema and .... a dinosaur film.

tick **one** box

go   see   ☐

went   see   ☐

went   saw   ☐

going   seeing   ☐

_____
1 mark

3. Circle the **adverb** in the sentence below.

Cautiously, Harriet crept down the creaky cellar stairs.

_____
1 mark

4. Read the passage below. Change all the underlined verbs
    from the **simple past** tense to the **simple present** tense.
    One has already been done for you.

Alison <u>made</u> jewellery in her workshop.

makes

Three squirrels <u>lived</u> in the big silver birch tree.

My sister <u>ate</u> too much bacon for breakfast.

We <u>drove</u> to the beach and <u>swam</u> in the sea.

_____
2 marks

5. Tick the sentence below that uses a **semi-colon** correctly.

tick **one** box

I was late for the meeting; I got lost on the way. ☐

However; only the yellow flowers arrived. ☐

Shani passed her driving test; Neil failed his. ☐

There's only one thing I'll eat on Friday nights; pizza. ☐

_____
1 mark

6. Read the sentence below.
Write a **synonym** for the word 'peculiar' in the box.

The <u>peculiar</u> thing was that the door didn't have a handle.

[   ]

1 mark

7. Put a tick in the correct column to show whether each sentence is in the **present progressive** or **past progressive** tense.

Sentence	Present progressive	Past progressive
Kate is having Arabic lessons.		
People were running past me.		
My mum is picking apples.		

1 mark

8. Tick the sentence below that has a **relative clause**.

tick **one** box

He likes camping but he doesn't like swimming. [ ]

I got it from a woman who lives round the corner. [ ]

Zoe kept walking until she got too tired. [ ]

That rollercoaster was the best one I've been on. [ ]

1 mark

9. Circle the **pronouns** in the sentence below.

I think we should collect our tickets from the station.

_____
1 mark

10. Read the sentences below.
Tick the sentence that uses a **co-ordinating conjunction**.

	tick **one** box
Omar read the newspaper while he waited.	☐
I was hungry, so I opened the fridge.	☐
You're nothing but trouble.	☐
She promised to come back as soon as she could.	☐

_____
1 mark

11. Explain how the **brackets** used below give the two sentences different meanings.

Ben's sisters who work long hours never answer the phone.

Ben's sisters (who work long hours) never answer the phone.

....

....

....

_____
1 mark

END OF TEST

/ 12

There are **12 questions** in this test. Give yourself **10 minutes** to answer them all.

1.   Circle all the words in the sentence below that should start
     with a **capital letter**.

     my friend chris and i went to manchester on saturday. _____

     1 mark

2.   Read the sentences below. Change all the underlined words
     from the **singular** to the **plural** form.
     One has already been done for you.

     My dad asked me to clean the <u>paintbrush</u>.

     paintbrushes

     He ate the <u>cherry</u> before I could stop him.

     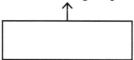

     I need a recipe to use up the <u>potato</u> I found in the cupboard.

     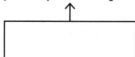

     _____
     1 mark

3. Look at the table below. Put a tick in each row to show which **punctuation mark** should be used at the end of each sentence.

Sentence	Question mark	Exclamation mark	Full stop
What wonderful news			
Are you going on holiday			
I wonder what the answer is			

1 mark

4. Circle the **noun** in the sentence below.

They all praised her for showing determination.

1 mark

5. Read the sentences below.
Explain how the use of a **hyphen** changes the meaning of the second sentence.

Gina bought an extra large carton of milk.

Gina bought an extra-large carton of milk.

....

....

....

1 mark

6.   Rewrite the sentences below as one sentence by using
     a **relative pronoun**.

     Natalie phoned her friend Diti. Diti lives in Germany.

     ....

     ....

     _____

     1 mark

7.   Draw a line to match each word below with an **antonym**.

     | elated | | minuscule |
     | immense | | unbroken |
     | shattered | | miserable |
     | noisy | | peaceful |

     _____

     1 mark

8.   Read the sentence below.
     Write the **present perfect form** of the underlined verb in the box.

     The children <u>drink</u> their glasses of milk.

     _____

     1 mark

9.   Circle the **modal verb** in the sentence below.

     Luca might mow the lawn next week if it's not raining.

     _____

     1 mark

10. The sentence below is missing two **commas**.
Tick **two** boxes to show where the commas should go.

My friends who are coming on the bus are going to be late.

↑ ↑ ↑ ↑ ↑

☐ ☐ ☐ ☐ ☐

_____
1 mark

11. Underline the **noun phrase** in the sentence below.

The dusty old motorbike that's been sitting in my grandpa's

garage for twenty years probably doesn't work any more.

_____
1 mark

12. Read the sentences below.
Tick the sentence that uses a **subordinating conjunction**.

tick **one** box

Neesha packed her passport and her sunglasses. ☐

It was early when they left, so they didn't have breakfast. ☐

Ailsa missed her flight because she was buying a pastry. ☐

She had to wait until 12 o'clock for the next one. ☐

_____
1 mark

END OF TEST

/ 12

There are **12 questions** in this test. Give yourself **10 minutes** to answer them all.

1.   Circle the **verb** in the sentence below.

Matt and Claire enjoyed the walk despite the rain.

1 mark

2.   Tick the sentence below that uses a **comma** correctly.

tick **one** box

Surjit's favourite meal is lasagne garlic bread, and salad.   ☐

Zara is going to Croatia in the holidays, Evan is going to Yorkshire.   ☐

Ava, who won the swimming race at the weekend is coming to my party.   ☐

Reluctantly, Elizabeth put her new guitar back in the cupboard.   ☐

1 mark

3.   Write an **exclamation** beginning with the word given below.

What ....

1 mark

4.   Read the sentence below.
     Insert a **dash** in the most appropriate place in the sentence.

Caitlin sat waiting on the stairs
all morning finally the doorbell rang.

1 mark

5. Put a tick in each row to show whether the sentence is **formal** or **informal**.

Sentence	Formal	Informal
It is crucial that you be ready at noon.		
We're going to the park later.		
I will endeavour to achieve my goal.		
This is the latest model, is it?		

1 mark

6. Tick the sentence that uses the **passive voice**.

tick **one** box

Amy went out for lunch on her birthday. ☐

The tradition was started by the Victorians. ☐

Kieran was walking up a mountain. ☐

Nobody expected Theo to come to the party. ☐

1 mark

7. For each verb below, write a suitable **prefix** on the line to make a new verb.

..............place

..............lead

..............run

1 mark

8.   The sentence below is missing a **colon**.
     Tick **one** box to show where the colon should go.

They were squashed in the back of the car they'd brought too

much luggage to fit in the boot.

_____
1 mark

9.   Write a sentence below that has **two** main clauses.

....

....   _____
                                                                                                    1 mark

10. Tick the sentence below that uses a **preposition**.

                                                                          tick **one** box

My sister is younger than I am.   ☐

Paula booked a table as she expected it to be busy.   ☐

Fraeya has lived in Bath since 2010.   ☐

The waterfall was really high.   ☐

_____
1 mark

11. Put a tick in the correct column to show whether each word in **bold** is the **subject** or the **object** of the sentence.

Sentence	Subject	Object
Kate picked up her **cat**.		
The **teacher** collected the children.		
Sarah met **Matt** when she was living in Clapham.		
They brought plenty for everyone.		

1 mark

12. Tick the box that shows how the underlined words are used in the sentence below.

Nathan didn't like the look of the cave at all. He decided he would get out of there <u>as soon as he could</u>.

tick **one** box

as a relative clause ☐

as a noun phrase ☐

as a prepositional phrase ☐

as an adverbial phrase ☐

1 mark

END OF TEST

/ 12

Set C: Spelling Test

For this test, you'll need someone to **read out** the transcript from the middle of the book, or you can use the **online audio file**. The test will take about 10 minutes.

mark box

1. A frog was .... across the garden. ☐

2. Jenny's baby brother is learning to .... ☐

3. The scout .... were a bit shabby. ☐

4. Shamir was doing a .... experiment. ☐

5. David looked .... at the chocolate cake. ☐

6. The .... came to fit some new plug sockets. ☐

7. Anita's kitchen table is an .... ☐

8. The travel agent gave them some holiday .... ☐

9. It's important to have enough .... in your diet. ☐

10. The farmer went to .... the field. ☐

11. Everyone at the ball looked very .... ☐

12. The fisherman was told not to .... ☐

/ 12

End of Set C: Scoresheet

You've finished a full set of tests — well done!

Now it's time to put your scores in here
and see how you're getting on.

	Score	
Test 1		/12
Test 2		/12
Test 3		/12
Test 4		/12
Spelling Test		/12
Total		**/60**

Once you've got a score out of 60, check it out in the table below...

0 – 29	If you got a lot of questions wrong, don't worry. Ask an adult to help you work out the **areas** you need **more practice** on. Then have another go at **this** set of tests.
30 – 45	If you got half-marks or better, you're doing well. **Read** back over your **incorrect** answers and make sure you know **why** they're wrong.
46 – 60	Woohoo! You've done really well — congratulations!

One last thing... bend your brain round this one:

Can you make five more **four letter words** from the letters in the word MARVELLOUS?

o v a l _ _ _ _ _ _ _ _ _ _ _ _ _ _ _ _ _ _ _ _

Hints and Tips

Grammar, punctuation and spelling can be a bit tricky.
If you get stuck, this page might help you out.

1. **Learn** the **main parts** of speech.

   The <u>cyclist</u> <u>pedalled</u> up the <u>steep</u> road.

   Noun   **Verb**   **Adjective**
   (a naming word)   (a doing or   (a describing word)
                     being word)

2. Make sure you can identify the different **parts** of a **sentence**.

   <u>While he was cycling,</u> <u>he thought about what to have for dinner</u>.

   Subordinate Clause   **Main Clause**
   (the less important clause)   (the most important clause)

3. Always use **capital letters** for proper nouns and after **full stops**,
   exclamation marks and **question marks**.

   Proper noun

   We're going to have a picnic**.** **W**hat a nice idea**!** **W**ould **A**my like to come too**?**

   Capital letter   **Full stop**   **Exclamation mark**   **Question mark**

4. **Apostrophes** show **missing letters**, or that something **belongs** to someone.

   I don't like the countryside.   Peter's bread.
   (This is a **contracted form** of 'do not'.)   (This is to show **possession**.)

5. **Break** words down into **smaller parts** to help you spell them.
   e.g. en-vi-ron-ment   fre-quen-cy   ap-pre-hen-sive

Answers

Set A

Test 1 — Pages 2-5

1. 1 mark

listened

2. 1 mark

On Mondays, Steven plays football in the park.

3. 1 mark for all three correct

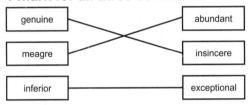

4. 1 mark

The dog <u>will</u> need a bath after going for a walk in the forest.

5. 1 mark

Answers may vary, for example:
mine, yours, his, hers

6. 1 mark

The netball team was going to be late: their bus had broken down.

7. 1 mark

<u>One of the children</u> wasn't listening.

8. 1 mark for both correct

behind
since

9. 1 mark

I asked, "Can we go shopping on Saturday?"

10. 1 mark

The frogs bullied the tadpoles.

11. 1 mark

people's votes

12. 1 mark for both correct

Verb	Adjective
succeed	successful
believe	**believable**
invent	**inventive**

Test 2 — Pages 6-9

1. 1 mark

won't

2. 1 mark

Where's the train station

3. 1 mark

Coralie found <u>Nigel</u>.

4. 1 mark

The library at the end of my street is closed on Wednesday afternoons; the library in town is closed on Monday afternoons.

5. 1 mark for both correct

The company apologised for the delay. There was a delay in getting the results.

6. 1 mark

They are making lunch for us.

7. 1 mark

I didn't want to take part in the school play <u>because I'm too shy</u>.

8. 1 mark

were   are

9. 1 mark

Answers may vary, for example:
The first sentence means that only the children who are blond enjoy swimming. The second sentence means that all the children are blond and they all enjoy swimming.

10. 1 mark

has written

11. 1 mark for all four correct

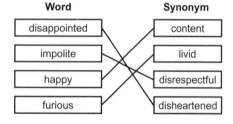

Word	Synonym
disappointed	content
impolite	livid
happy	disrespectful
furious	disheartened

12. 1 mark

Answers may vary, for example:
My cat was lying on the sofa.

Test 3 — Pages 10-13

1. 1 mark

There was a red box lying on the floor.

2. 1 mark

Francis enjoys going for walks in the countryside, even though he has a bad knee.

3. 1 mark

Answers may vary, for example:
We could go shopping, or we could go bowling.

4. 1 mark

I made a fruit salad using melons

grapes and strawberries.

5. 1 mark

I played tennis and then I went out for a meal.

6. 1 mark

who

7. 1 mark

Before he could stop me, I snatched a cake and ate it.

8. 1 mark for all three correct

Sentence	Command	Statement
You could take the rubbish out.		✓
Water the plants.	✓	
My brother washes the car.		✓
Lily, put those books away.	✓	

9. 1 mark

Answers may vary, for example:
The first sentence means that Sally had to hand in weekly reports and there were four of them. The second sentence means that Sally had to hand in a report every four weeks.

10. 1 mark

Answers may vary, for example:
Perhaps, Maybe

11. 1 mark for all four correct

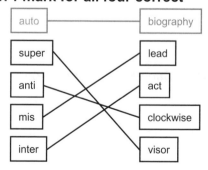

auto	biography
super	lead
anti	act
mis	clockwise
inter	visor

Answers

12. 1 mark for both correct

If I were you, I would enter the competition.
I wish I were able to go with you.

Test 4 — Pages 14-17

1. 1 mark

were

2. 1 mark for all three correct

It was warm, so the team were playing

all of their matches on the field.

3. 1 mark

What an enormous cow that is!

4. 1 mark

Since

5. 1 mark for all three correct

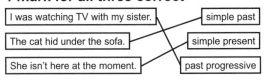

6. 1 mark

Tidy your bedroom after you've washed the dishes.

7. 1 mark for all three correct

She, herself, our

8. 1 mark

My auntie, who lives in France, likes to visit the market.

9. 1 mark

Hartford is the state capital of Connecticut — it's about halfway between New York and Boston.

10. 1 mark for all three correct

Taylor gently stroked her cat — they

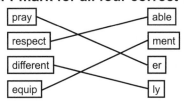

were both relaxed.

11. 1 mark

We went to the beach (I forgot my sun hat, as usual) and spent the afternoon swimming and sunbathing.

12. 1 mark for all four correct

pray	able
respect	ment
different	er
equip	ly

Spelling Test — Page 18

For full sentence answers, see the pull-out transcripts in the middle of the book.

1. 1 mark

ladies

2. 1 mark

weigh

3. 1 mark

currency

4. 1 mark

perfectly

5. 1 mark

allowed

6. 1 mark

misspell

7. 1 mark

pyramid

8. 1 mark

discussion

9. 1 mark

infectious

10. 1 mark

irregular

11. 1 mark

receipt

12. 1 mark

compliment

Scoresheet Question — Page 19

We <u>were</u> going to a museum <u>where</u> we could <u>wear</u> clothes from the Tudor period.

Set B

Test 1 — Pages 20-23

1. 1 mark for both correct

have
anything

2. 1 mark for both correct

Did you notice the sign on the door?
It took them a week to notice.

3. 1 mark

Answers may vary, for example:
an, a, the

4. 1 mark for both correct

While Nate is shopping, <u>Liza takes the dog for a walk</u>.
<u>I didn't buy a handbag</u>, although I did see one that I liked.

5. 1 mark

Answers may vary, for example:
Can you turn off the television?

6. 1 mark for all three correct

Sentence	Active	Passive
They were surprised by the response.		✓
I was welcomed by the head teacher.		✓
The man juggled with the apples.	✓	
I dragged my suitcase down the street.	✓	

7. 1 mark

I shouted, "Watch out for that dog!"

8. 1 mark

Nadiya was walking home.

9. 1 mark

when, <u>and</u>

10. 1 mark

Answers will vary, for example:
The first sentence is asking someone if they're going to tell Gareth, but the second sentence is asking Gareth if he's going to tell.

11. 1 mark

anxious, confident

12. 1 mark for all three correct

Sentence	Conjunction	Preposition
I'll take an umbrella <u>as</u> it's raining.	✓	
She bought it <u>as</u> a present.		✓
He waved <u>as</u> he left the room.	✓	

Answers

Test 2 — Pages 24-27

1. 1 mark

Becky likes carrot cake, doesn't she

2. 1 mark

The wind howled as James wrapped his scarf tighter. He was looking forward to getting home and warming up.

3. 1 mark for all three correct

runs, ran, was

4. 1 mark

Luis bought himself a bike he had just

been paid.

5. 1 mark

I couldn't reach the book on the top shelf.

6. 1 mark for all three correct

so, whilst, since

7. 1 mark

The librarian

8. 1 mark

As quietly as possible, I crept out of the room.

9. 1 mark

have auditioned

10. 1 mark

endangered

11. 1 mark

were

12. 1 mark

empty

Test 3 — Pages 28-31

1. 1 mark

I went to the shops and bought a pen, some trousers, a T-shirt, a pair of shoes and a DVD.

2. 1 mark

Afterwards

3. 1 mark

asked   wrote

4. 1 mark for all three correct

and, but, or

5. 1 mark

Colon

6. 1 mark

Answers may vary, for example:
I went for a walk.

7. 1 mark

Angel Falls — which is in Venezuela — is the highest waterfall in the world.

8. 1 mark

ise

9. 1 mark for all three correct

Sentence	Adjective	Adverb
Elliot is a good singer.	✓	
She acted well in the play.		✓
That exercise is really easy.	✓	

10. 1 mark

which

11. 1 mark

I stayed up watching television until it was late.

Answers

12. 1 mark

The final was watched on television by over a million people.

Test 4 — Pages 32-35

1. 1 mark for both correct

Words	Contracted form
we have	we've
he has	**he's**
will not	**won't**

2. 1 mark for all three correct

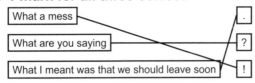

3. 1 mark

They, she

4. 1 mark

*care**ful***

5. 1 mark

could

1 mark

possibility

6. 1 mark

belief

7. 1 mark

rolled

8. 1 mark

My grandad walks <u>with a limp</u> — he has an old injury.

9. 1 mark for any correct answer with <u>consistent</u> punctuation and capitalisation, e.g.

Things I need to do:
- *wash the dishes*
- *tidy my room*
- *take the dog for a walk*

Answers with commas or semi-colons after each of the first two items and a full stop after the third are also acceptable. The use of a capital letter at the start of every item is also acceptable.

10. 1 mark

The tomatoes were eaten by Tom.

11. 1 mark

I ate fish, chips and peas on Monday; a chicken wrap on Tuesday; and potatoes, sausages and beans on Wednesday.

Spelling Test — Page 36

For full sentence answers, see the pull-out transcripts in the middle of the book.

1. 1 mark

quiet

2. 1 mark

nature

3. 1 mark

division

4. 1 mark

couple

5. 1 mark

sensation

6. 1 mark

character

Answers

7. 1 mark

preferably

8. 1 mark

creation

9. 1 mark

curious

10. 1 mark

partial

11. 1 mark

responsibly

12. 1 mark

muscles

Scoresheet Question — Page 37

A AM HAM SHAM SHAME SHAMED ASHAMED

Set C

Test 1 — Pages 38-41

1. 1 mark

Put that down right now

2. 1 mark

"That's a really nice backpack," said Nita.

3. 1 mark

Put the lid on before you shake it.

4. 1 mark

messier

5. 1 mark

I borrowed Rob's armbands for swimming.

6. 1 mark

Are bluebells usually found in wooded areas?

7. 1 mark

Last night I read my book <u>until</u> I fell asleep.

8. 1 mark

Answers may vary, for example:
hers

9. 1 mark for all four correct

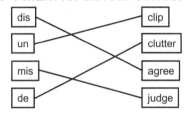

10. 1 mark for both correct

<u>Arthur made Kirstie pancakes</u> on her birthday.
Before Kamil went to Rome, <u>he bought an Italian dictionary</u>.

11. 1 mark

Turn off the light before he sees us!

12. 1 mark for all three correct

floral, florist, flowers

Test 2 — Pages 42-45

1. 1 mark

Tony and Will spent ages pulling up weeds in the garden last Saturday. It looked much better when they were finished.

2. 1 mark

went saw

3. 1 mark

Cautiously

Answers

**4. 1 mark for two or three correct
2 marks for all four correct**

live
eats
drive
swim

5. 1 mark

Shani passed her driving test;
Neil failed his.

6. 1 mark

Answers may vary, for example:
strange

7. 1 mark for all three correct

Sentence	Present progressive	Past progressive
Kate is having Arabic lessons.	✓	
People were running past me.		✓
My mum is picking apples.	✓	

8. 1 mark

I got it from a woman who lives round the corner.

9. 1 mark for all three correct

I, we, our

10. 1 mark

I was hungry, so I opened the fridge.

11. 1 mark

Answers may vary, for example:
The first sentence means that some of Ben's sisters work long hours, and those sisters never answer the phone. The second sentence means that all of Ben's sisters work long hours and never answer the phone.

Test 3 — Pages 46-49

1. 1 mark for all five correct

my, chris, i, manchester, saturday

2. 1 mark for both correct

cherry — cherries
potato — potatoes

3. 1 mark for all three correct

Sentence	Question mark	Exclamation mark	Full stop
What wonderful news		✓	
Are you going on holiday	✓		
I wonder what the answer is			✓

4. 1 mark

determination

5. 1 mark

Answers may vary, for example:
The first sentence means that Gina bought another large carton of milk. The second sentence means that Gina bought a carton of milk that was size extra-large.

6. 1 mark

Natalie phoned her friend Diti, who lives in Germany.

7. 1 mark for all four correct

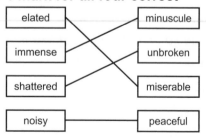

8. 1 mark

have drunk

Answers

9. 1 mark

might

10. 1 mark for both correct

My friends who are coming on the bus

are going to be late.

11. 1 mark

<u>The dusty old motorbike that's been sitting in my grandpa's garage for twenty years</u> *probably doesn't work any more.*

12. 1 mark

Ailsa missed her flight because she was buying a pastry.

Test 4 — Pages 50-53

1. 1 mark

enjoyed

2. 1 mark

Reluctantly, Elizabeth put her new guitar back in the cupboard.

3. 1 mark

Answers may vary, for example:
What a surprise!

4. 1 mark

Caitlin sat waiting on the stairs all morning — finally the doorbell rang.

5. 1 mark for all four correct

Sentence	Formal	Informal
It is crucial that you be ready at noon.	✓	
We're going to the park later.		✓
I will endeavour to achieve my goal.	✓	
This is the latest model, is it?		✓

6. 1 mark

The tradition was started by the Victorians.

7. 1 mark for all three correct

Answers may vary, for example:
replace
mislead
overrun

8. 1 mark

They were squashed in the back of the car they'd brought too much luggage to

fit in the boot.

9. 1 mark

Answers may vary, for example:
We went to the cinema and then we went out for dinner.

10. 1 mark

Fraeya has lived in Bath since 2010.

11. 1 mark for all four correct

Sentence	Subject	Object
Kate picked up her **cat**.		✓
The **teacher** collected the children.	✓	
Sarah met **Matt** when she was living in Clapham.		✓
They brought plenty for everyone.	✓	

12. 1 mark

as an adverbial phrase

Answers

Spelling Test — Page 54

For full sentence answers, see the pull-out transcripts in the middle of the book.

1. **1 mark**
   hopping

2. **1 mark**
   crawl

3. **1 mark**
   headquarters

4. **1 mark**
   science

5. **1 mark**
   hungrily

6. **1 mark**
   electrician

7. **1 mark**
   antique

8. **1 mark**
   brochures

9. **1 mark**
   protein

10. **1 mark**
    plough

11. **1 mark**
    glamorous

12. **1 mark**
    exaggerate

Scoresheet Question — Page 55

Answers may vary, for example:
over, roll, role, sole, vole, mole, meal, seal, real, veal, male, sale, vale, move, love, rove, rave, save, user, mare